The flying carpet

A playscript
adapted from a story by
Roderick Hunt

by Jacquie Buttriss and Ann Callander

Characters
Narrator
Biff
Dad *and* **Boy**
Kipper

Scene 1

Narrator Scene 1 'The old carpet'
Biff's carpet was torn.

Biff It has a big hole in it.

Narrator Biff showed Dad.

Dad Sorry, Biff.
We can't afford a new one.

Narrator	Biff and Kipper went to the junk shop with Dad.
Kipper	Can I have a bookcase for my room, please?
Dad	I'll get this one for you.
Biff	Can I have this old carpet, please?

Narrator Dad looked at the old carpet.

Dad You don't want that old thing.

Kipper It's old and dirty.

Biff I like it.
Please may I have it?

Dad Yes, as long as it doesn't cost too much.

Narrator Biff beat the carpet.

(sound of beating)

Dad I didn't think a carpet would be so dusty.

Kipper I wonder who had it last.

Biff Someone who didn't wipe their feet.

Narrator Biff and Dad gave the carpet a shampoo.

Dad It looks better already.

Biff It looks beautiful.

Dad It looks quite old, so maybe it's worth a lot of money.

Scene 2

Narrator Scene 2 'A new kind of adventure'
Biff was in her bedroom reading
a book.
Kipper came in.

Kipper Can I read to you, Biff?

Biff Look. The magic key is glowing.

Kipper Help! The carpet is flying.

(sound of magic)

Biff This is a new kind of adventure.

Kipper I hope we don't fall off.

Narrator The carpet flew on and on.
It flew over deserts and mountains.

Biff I wonder where we're going?

Kipper The carpet is slowing down.
It's flying over a town.

Biff I've never seen a town like
this one.

Kipper I wonder if we're going to land.

Scene 3

Narrator Scene 3 'The boy in the tower'
The carpet stopped by a window at the top of the tower.

Biff Look. There's a little boy.

Kipper He's crying.
He looks very unhappy.

(sound of crying)

Biff He must be a prisoner.

Narrator Biff and Kipper climbed into the room.
The boy jumped up in surprise.

Kipper Why are you locked up in this tower?

Boy I am the king of this land.
But my wicked uncle locked me
in this tower.

Kipper Why did he lock you in?

Boy He was jealous.
He wanted to be king instead.

Biff Where is your mother?

Boy She ran to the mountains and
took her army with her.

Kipper Your uncle is a bad man.

Boy Yes. He is cruel and greedy.

Biff Can your mother help you?

Boy She will not give the order to attack.
She is afraid my uncle will harm me.

Scene 4

Narrator Scene 4 'Make a wish'

Biff We must set you free.
The carpet will take us to your mother.

Kipper We can help you.
Climb out of the window.

Narrator Then they all sat on the carpet.

Boy How do we make it fly?

Kipper How will it know where to take us?

Biff Make a wish.
Then it'll go where we want it to.

Narrator They made a wish and the carpet zoomed off towards the mountains.

(zooming sound)

Biff It's slowing down.

Kipper I hope it knows where to land.

Boy It looks a long way down.

Narrator The carpet landed safely.

(sound of a gentle bump)

Boy Look. There's my mother.

Narrator When the boy's mother saw him, she couldn't believe her eyes.

Kipper His mother looks happy to see him.

Scene 5

Narrator	Scene 5 'The big battle' The boy's mother called all her soldiers.
Boy	I'm free. Now we can attack the city.
Kipper	You can be king again.

Narrator The soldiers came down from the mountains.
There was a big battle.

(sounds of battle)

Kipper Let's watch the battle.

Biff We can watch from here.

Boy It's a safe place.

Narrator When the battle was over everyone was pleased that the boy was king again.

Boy My wicked uncle must be punished.

Biff Look. There he is.

Boy Oh no! He's getting away.

(sound of a horse galloping)

Kipper How can we stop him?

Scene 6

Narrator Scene 6 'Stop him!'
Biff made a wish and the magic carpet flew after the wicked uncle.

(zooming sound)

Boy My uncle is riding as fast as he can.

Kipper But the carpet is faster.

Boy Stop him!

Narrator The magic carpet pulled the wicked uncle from his horse.

Biff Look. It's rolling him back to the city.

Narrator Biff and Kipper took the wicked uncle back to the boy.

Boy Now it's my uncle's turn to go to prison.

Narrator The boy gave Biff and Kipper a present.

Kipper What a beautiful toy camel.

Biff Thank you.

Kipper The magic key is glowing.

Biff It's time for us to go, but we'll take our carpet if you don't mind.

Scene 7

Narrator Scene 7 'You'll be lucky'
The magic took Biff and Kipper home.

(sound of magic working)

Biff What an adventure!

Kipper If I wish very hard will the carpet take me to school each day?

Biff You'll be lucky!

Printed in Hong Kong